DEEP
INTO THE
AMAZON
JUNGLE

Also in the
Fabien Cousteau Expeditions

GREAT WHITE SHARK ADVENTURE

JOURNEY UNDER THE ARCTIC

FABIEN COUSTEAU
EXPEDITIONS

DEEP
INTO THE
AMAZON
JUNGLE

WRITTEN BY

JAMES O. FRAIOLI

ILLUSTRATED BY

JOE ST.PIERRE

MARGARET K. McELDERRY BOOKS

NEW YORK   LONDON   TORONTO   SYDNEY   NEW DELHI

AUTHORS' NOTE

Deep into the Amazon Jungle is a work of fiction
based on actual expeditions and accepted ideas
about the Amazon and its inhabitants.

MARGARET K. McELDERRY BOOKS
An imprint of Simon & Schuster Children's Publishing Division
1230 Avenue of the Americas, New York, New York 10020
Text © 2021 by Fabien Cousteau and James O. Fraioli
Illustrations © 2021 by Joseph St.Pierre
Case design by Tom Daly © 2021 by Simon & Schuster, Inc.
MARGARET K. McELDERRY BOOKS is a trademark of Simon & Schuster, Inc.
For information about special discounts for bulk purchases, please contact Simon & Schuster
Special Sales at 1-866-506-1949 or business@simonandschuster.com.
The Simon & Schuster Speakers Bureau can bring authors to your live event.
For more information or to book an event, contact the Simon & Schuster Speakers
Bureau at 1-866-248-3049 or visit our website at www.simonspeakers.com.
Also available in a Margaret K. McElderry Books hardcover edition
Interior design by Tom Daly
The text for this book was set in Chaparral Pro.
The illustrations for this book were rendered digitally.
Manufactured in China
0221 SCP
This Margaret K. McElderry Books paper-over-board proprietary edition March 2021
10 9 8 7 6 5 4 3 2 1
CIP data for this book is available from the Library of Congress.
ISBN 978-1-5344-2093-9 (paper over board)
ISBN 978-1-5344-2094-6 (hardcover)
ISBN 978-1-5344-2095-3 (eBook)
ISBN 978-1-6659-0187-1 (Literati paper-over-board proprietary)

TO THE EFFORTS AND INDIVIDUALS WHO WORK DILIGENTLY
TO PROTECT AND PRESERVE THE AMAZON RAINFOREST
AND ITS DIVERSE ECOSYSTEMS.

DEEP
INTO THE
AMAZON
JUNGLE

THE AMAZON RIVER IS MORE THAN *11* MILLION YEARS OLD AND SURROUNDS THE ENTIRE AMAZON RAINFOREST.

THE RIVER IS APPROXIMATELY *4,000* MILES LONG AND IS THE SECOND-LONGEST RIVER IN THE WORLD. THE NILE RIVER IN AFRICA IS THE LONGEST.

THE AMAZON RAINFOREST IS A MASSIVE TROPICAL FOREST THAT WAS FORMED *55* MILLION YEARS AGO.

A TROPICAL RAINFOREST IS A FOREST WITH TALL TREES, A WARM CLIMATE, AND LOTS OF RAIN.

TODAY, THIS ANCIENT RAINFOREST IS MORE THAN 2 MILLION SQUARE MILES, MAKING IT THE LARGEST ON THE PLANET. THE RAINFOREST ALSO SUPPORTS AND NURTURES THE RICHEST ECOSYSTEM ON EARTH.

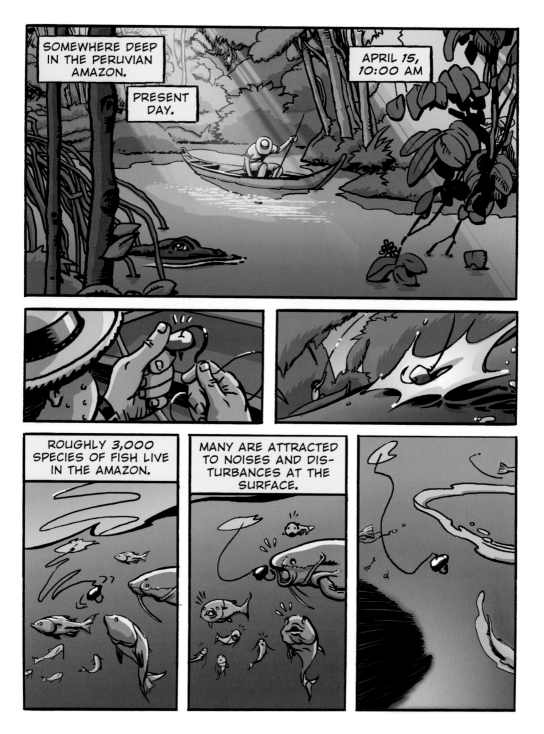

4

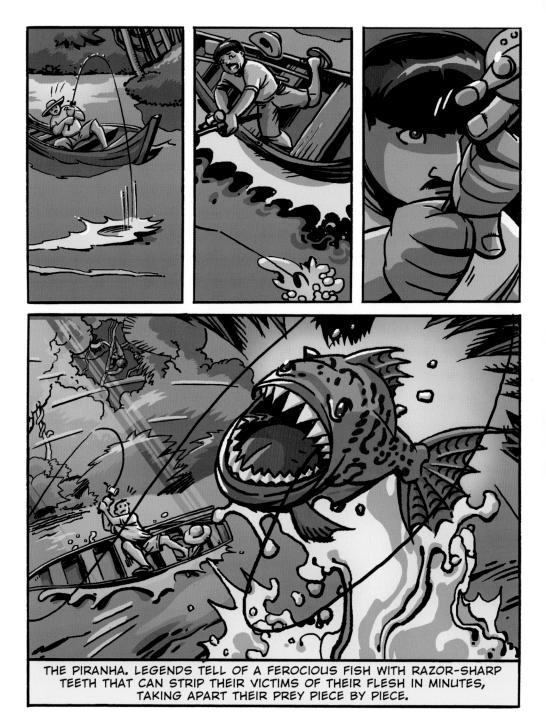

THE PIRANHA. LEGENDS TELL OF A FEROCIOUS FISH WITH RAZOR-SHARP TEETH THAT CAN STRIP THEIR VICTIMS OF THEIR FLESH IN MINUTES, TAKING APART THEIR PREY PIECE BY PIECE.

THERE ARE BETWEEN 40 AND 60 DIFFERENT KINDS OF PIRANHAS IN *12* DIFFERENT SCIENTIFIC FAMILIES.

NEW SPECIES OF FISH, INCLUDING PIRANHAS, CONTINUE TO BE DISCOVERED IN THE AMAZON.

SOME PIRANHAS HAVE A REPUTATION FOR KILLING AND EATING ANYTHING THAT ENTERS THE WATER AND CROSSES THEIR PATH.

THE BELÉN MARKET IS A HUGE OUT-DOOR SUPERMARKET THAT COVERS MORE THAN *20* CITY BLOCKS.

CH-CLICK!

CH-CLICK!

EVERYTHING CAN BE BOUGHT AND SOLD HERE, INCLUDING MANY SUPPLIES TO OUTFIT AN EXPEDITION INTO THE AMAZON.

CH-CLICK!

10

HEY, FABIEN.
HI.
WHAT ARE YOU DOING, FABIEN?
CH-CLICK!
AS I BRIEFLY SHARED WITH YOU YESTERDAY, WE'RE ON AN EXCITING MISSION TO HUNT DOWN A MYSTERIOUS PIRANHA.
SO COOL!
COOL, IN-DEED. BUT THESE ARE LIKE NO OTHER.
CH-CLICK!
DISTURBING RUMORS ARE STILL FLOATING AROUND ABOUT A FISHERMAN WHO ENCOUNTERED A SCHOOL OF GIANT PIRANHAS WITH JAGUAR-LIKE MARKINGS IN A REMOTE AREA OF THE AMAZON.
WHOA!
COMMUNITY LEADERS HAVE ASKED US TO FIND OUT IF THESE PIRANHAS ARE REAL, AND IF SO, ARE THEY DANGEROUS.
IF THEY ARE, LOCAL OFFICIALS WILL NEED TO MAKE SURE EVERYONE IS SAFE UNTIL WE KNOW MORE.

I'M HOPING TO SEE IF ONE OF THOSE STRANGE PIRANHAS TURNS UP HERE THIS MORNING, WHICH WOULD QUICKLY PROVE THEIR EXISTENCE, BUT I'M NOT HAVING ANY LUCK.

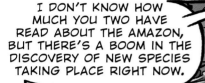

I DON'T KNOW HOW MUCH YOU TWO HAVE READ ABOUT THE AMAZON, BUT THERE'S A BOOM IN THE DISCOVERY OF NEW SPECIES TAKING PLACE RIGHT NOW.

AT THE SAME TIME, OUR PLANET IS ENTERING A NEW CHAPTER IN ITS HISTORY.

WHAT CHAPTER IS THAT?

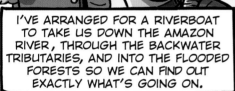

A TIME MARKED BY THE SIGNIFICANT GLOBAL IMPACT THAT HUMANS ARE HAVING ON THE EARTH'S FRAGILE ECOSYSTEM.

I'VE ARRANGED FOR A RIVERBOAT TO TAKE US DOWN THE AMAZON RIVER, THROUGH THE BACKWATER TRIBUTARIES, AND INTO THE FLOODED FORESTS SO WE CAN FIND OUT EXACTLY WHAT'S GOING ON.

LET'S GRAB SOME SUNSCREEN, BUG SPRAY, AND FISHHOOKS.

THEN WE'LL HEAD OVER TO THE BOAT AND I'LL INTRODUCE YOU TO THE REST OF THE CREW.

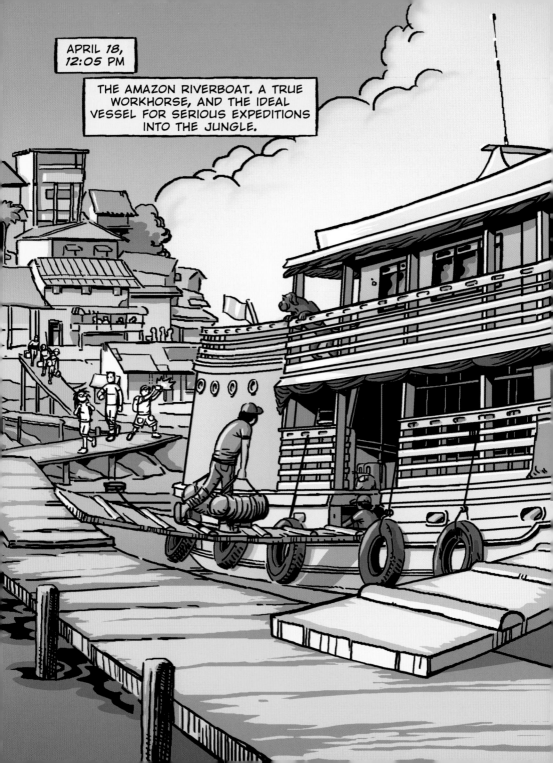

Type of Vessel: River cruise
Year of Construction: 2019
Port: Iquitos
Ship's Registry: Peru
Capacity: Up to 16 passengers
Crew: Captain and 4 staff

B/F RITA

14

17

FRANCISCO DE ORELLANA, A 16TH-CENTURY SPANISH EXPLORER, WAS THE FIRST EUROPEAN TO SAIL DEEP INTO THE AMAZON RIVER WHILE IN SEARCH OF GOLD AND CINNAMON. DURING HIS SEVEN-MONTH JOURNEY, FRANCISCO WAS ATTACKED BY WHAT HE BELIEVED WERE ARMED WOMEN. INSPIRED BY HIS DANGEROUS ENCOUNTER, FRANCISCO NAMED THE RIVER "AMAZON," AFTER THE RACE OF FEMALE WARRIORS IN ANCIENT GREEK MYTHOLOGY.

IN 2007, WORLD-RECORD MARATHON SWIMMER MARTIN STREL SWAM THE ENTIRE LENGTH OF THE AMAZON RIVER. HE SWAM UP TO 10 HOURS A DAY FOR 66 DAYS.

AFTER CAPTAINING THE SHIP *NIÑA* DURING CHRISTOPHER COLUMBUS'S FIRST VOYAGE TO THE NEW WORLD, SPANIARD VICENTE YÁÑEZ PINZÓN WAS OUT AT SEA WHEN HE REALIZED HE WAS SUDDENLY IN FRESHWATER. HE TURNED THE VESSEL AND HEADED FOR SHORE TO FIND THE SOURCE, WHICH LED HIM TO THE MOUTH OF THE AMAZON, WHICH HE NICKNAMED THE "SWEET SEA."

20

24

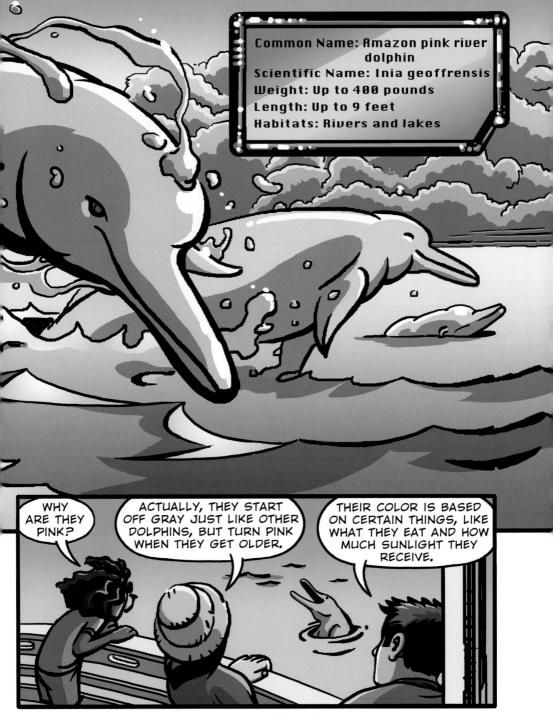

Common Name: Amazon pink river dolphin
Scientific Name: Inia geoffrensis
Weight: Up to 400 pounds
Length: Up to 9 feet
Habitats: Rivers and lakes

WHY ARE THEY PINK?

ACTUALLY, THEY START OFF GRAY JUST LIKE OTHER DOLPHINS, BUT TURN PINK WHEN THEY GET OLDER.

THEIR COLOR IS BASED ON CERTAIN THINGS, LIKE WHAT THEY EAT AND HOW MUCH SUNLIGHT THEY RECEIVE.

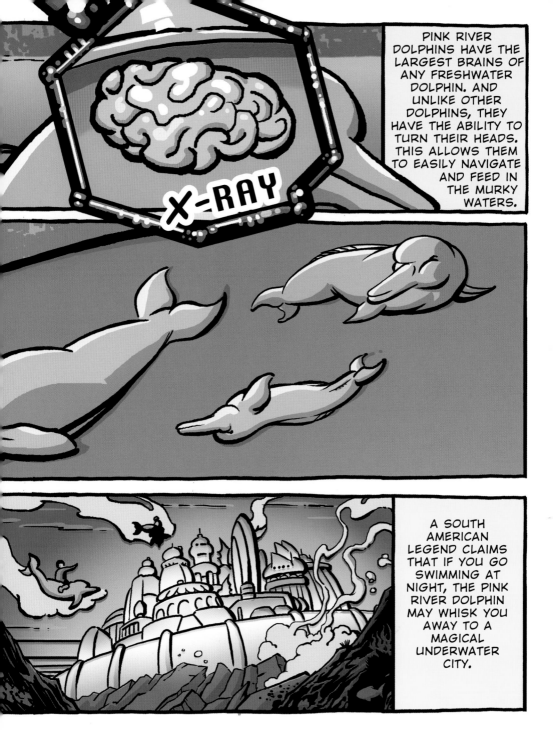

PINK RIVER DOLPHINS HAVE THE LARGEST BRAINS OF ANY FRESHWATER DOLPHIN. AND UNLIKE OTHER DOLPHINS, THEY HAVE THE ABILITY TO TURN THEIR HEADS. THIS ALLOWS THEM TO EASILY NAVIGATE AND FEED IN THE MURKY WATERS.

X-RAY

A SOUTH AMERICAN LEGEND CLAIMS THAT IF YOU GO SWIMMING AT NIGHT, THE PINK RIVER DOLPHIN MAY WHISK YOU AWAY TO A MAGICAL UNDERWATER CITY.

27

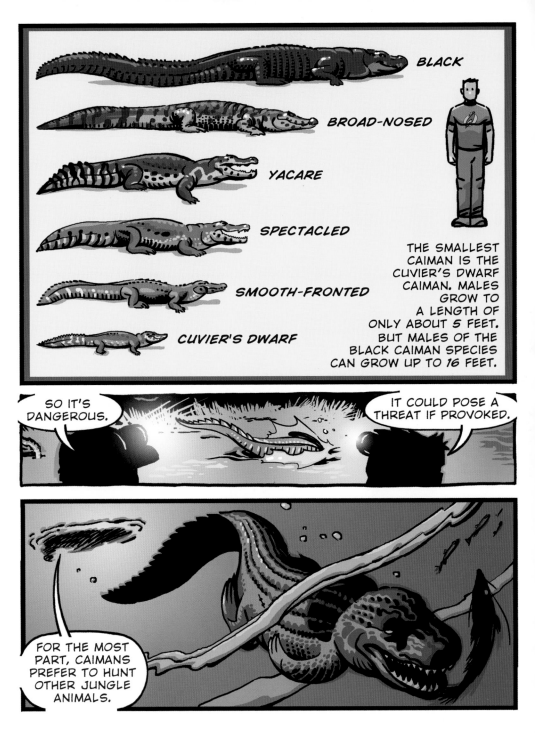

BLACK

BROAD-NOSED

YACARE

SPECTACLED

SMOOTH-FRONTED

CUVIER'S DWARF

THE SMALLEST CAIMAN IS THE CUVIER'S DWARF CAIMAN. MALES GROW TO A LENGTH OF ONLY ABOUT 5 FEET. BUT MALES OF THE BLACK CAIMAN SPECIES CAN GROW UP TO *16* FEET.

SO IT'S DANGEROUS.

IT COULD POSE A THREAT IF PROVOKED.

FOR THE MOST PART, CAIMANS PREFER TO HUNT OTHER JUNGLE ANIMALS.

THEY LOOK LIKE VAMPIRE BATS.

SERIOUSLY?

DON'T BE ALARMED. VAMPIRE BATS, LIKE MANY CREATURES WE'LL ENCOUNTER IN THE AMAZON, HAVE A BIT OF A BAD REPUTATION.

THE DOCTOR'S RIGHT. ALTHOUGH VAMPIRE BATS DRINK BLOOD, THEY PREFER BLOOD FROM ANIMALS LIKE COWS, PIGS, AND HORSES.

VAMPIRE BATS ARE THE ONLY MAMMALS IN THE WORLD THAT CAN LIVE FROM CONSUMING NOTHING ELSE BUT BLOOD.

VAMPIRE BATS ALSO HAVE HEAT SENSORS ON THEIR NOSES TO HELP THEM FIND A GOOD SPOT TO FEED ON THE ANIMAL, ESPECIALLY WHILE IT'S SLEEPING.

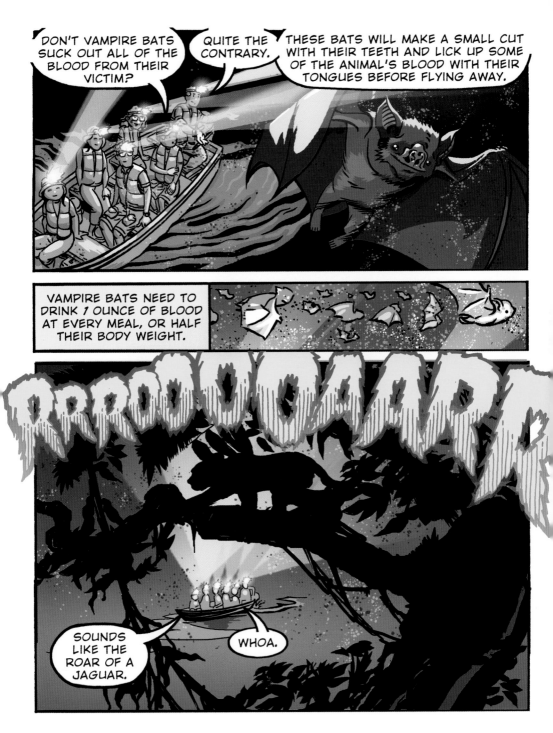

JAGUARS ARE AMONG THE MOST ENDANGERED AND DEADLIEST AMAZON RAINFOREST ANIMALS.

THEY ARE ALSO THE LARGEST OF SOUTH AMERICA'S BIG CATS AND THE THIRD-LARGEST CAT IN THE WORLD.

UNLIKE MOST BIG CATS, JAGUARS LOVE THE WATER—THEY OFTEN SWIM, BATHE, PLAY, AND EVEN HUNT FOR FISH IN STREAMS AND POOLS.

JAGUARS HAVE VERY POWERFUL JAWS, STRONG ENOUGH TO CRACK A TURTLE'S SHELL.

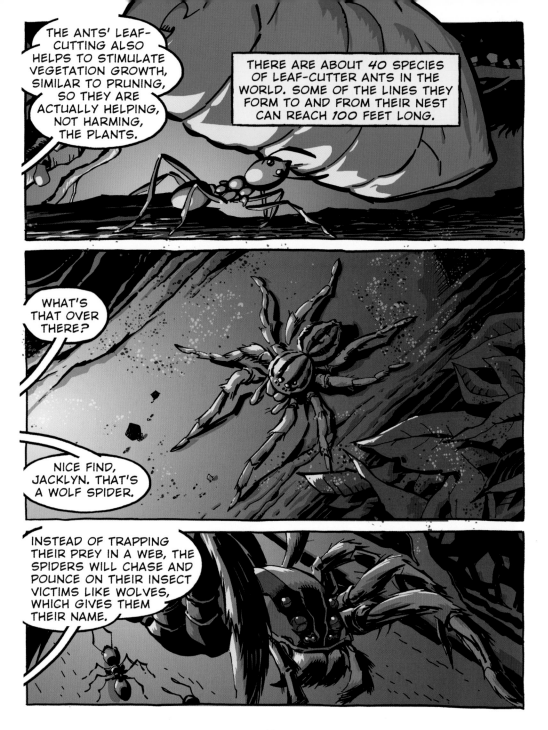

THE ANTS' LEAF-CUTTING ALSO HELPS TO STIMULATE VEGETATION GROWTH, SIMILAR TO PRUNING, SO THEY ARE ACTUALLY HELPING, NOT HARMING, THE PLANTS.

THERE ARE ABOUT *40* SPECIES OF LEAF-CUTTER ANTS IN THE WORLD. SOME OF THE LINES THEY FORM TO AND FROM THEIR NEST CAN REACH *100* FEET LONG.

WHAT'S THAT OVER THERE?

NICE FIND, JACKLYN. THAT'S A WOLF SPIDER.

INSTEAD OF TRAPPING THEIR PREY IN A WEB, THE SPIDERS WILL CHASE AND POUNCE ON THEIR INSECT VICTIMS LIKE WOLVES, WHICH GIVES THEM THEIR NAME.

40

SCORPIONS ARE CLOSELY RELATED TO SPIDERS. THEY ARE COMMONLY THOUGHT OF AS DESERT DWELLERS, BUT THEY ALSO LIVE IN THE DARK JUNGLES OF THE AMAZON. THERE ARE APPROXIMATELY 2,000 SPECIES OF SCORPIONS, BUT ONLY A HANDFUL OF THEM ARE DEADLY.

HOW MANY SPECIES

MORE THAN
400 MAMMALS

MORE THAN
3,000 FISH

44

AND OUR FISH HAVE ATTRACTED A LARGE FAMILY OF CAIMANS MOVING IN FAST.
BEST WE HEAD BACK TO THE *RITA* AND HAVE A GOOD NIGHT'S SLEEP BEFORE LEAVING TOMORROW FOR THE DEEPER REACHES OF THE AMAZON.

APRIL *19*, 10:04 AM

WELCOME TO LAKE SABANO.

THIS IS A PERMANENT FLOODED FOREST AND A FISH BREEDING GROUND FOR MANY SPECIES THAT THRIVE IN THE AMAZON. IF THOSE STRANGE PIRANHAS EXIST, WE SHOULD FIND THEM HERE.

FLOODED FORESTS OCCUR DURING THE "WET" SEASON, WHEN SNOW FROM THE MOUNTAINS MELTS AND MAKES ITS WAY INTO THE RIVER SYSTEM. AS THE EXCESS WATER MOVES DOWNSTREAM IT BEGINS TO FILL THE LOWER ECOSYSTEMS OF THE AMAZON FOREST, EVENTUALLY CAUSING CERTAIN AREAS TO FLOOD.

WHAT PRETTY BIRDS.

THEY'RE MACAWS.

ONE OF THE MOST COLORFUL BIRDS YOU'LL SEE IN THE PERUVIAN AMAZON.

MORE OFTEN THAN NOT YOU'LL HEAR THEM SQUAWKING LOUDLY LONG BEFORE THEY COME INTO SIGHT.

LOOK AT ALL THAT SMOKE BEHIND THEM.

IT'S LIKELY ANOTHER FOREST FIRE.

SADLY, THE RAINFOREST IS BURNING AT A RATE WE'VE NEVER SEEN BEFORE.

AND THAT'S TERRIBLE NEWS SINCE THE AMAZON RAINFOREST IS THE "LUNGS OF THE EARTH."

WHAT FABIEN MEANS IS THE AMAZON HOLDS A MASSIVE AMOUNT OF THE WORLD'S OXYGEN, ABOUT 20 PERCENT.

EIGHTY PERCENT OF THE FOREST CLEARED IN THE AMAZON IS FROM CATTLE RANCHING.

MAYBE WE SHOULDN'T BE EATING SO MANY HAMBURGERS.

THAT'S DEFINITELY A START. EATING FEWER BURGERS WILL HELP DECREASE THE DEMAND AND CUT BACK ON THE PRESSURE TO CLEAR MORE FORESTS.

AN AREA IN THE AMAZON THE SIZE OF IRELAND HAS ALSO BEEN CLEARED FOR GROWING SOYBEAN, WHICH IS SHIPPED AROUND THE WORLD TO FEED CATTLE AND SUPPORT THE BEEF INDUSTRY.

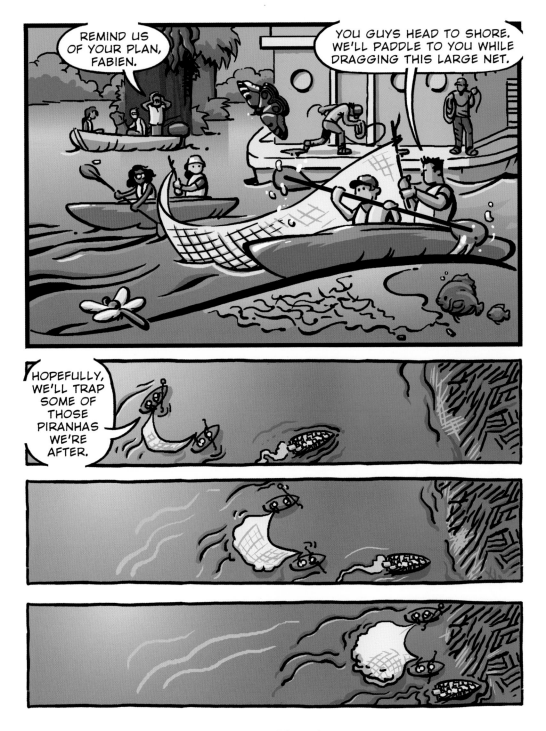

EVERYONE, PLEASE BE CAREFUL. I CAN SEE WE HAVE SOME EXCITING FISH TO OBSERVE, BUT ALSO VERY DANGEROUS ONES.

CAN YOU POINT OUT THE DANGEROUS FISH?

THAT ONE IS A STINGRAY. THEY LIVE IN THE AMAZON RIVER SYSTEM AND ARE ONE OF THE ONLY RAYS THAT LIVE IN FRESH-WATER.

THE TAILS OF THE FRESHWATER STINGRAY CONTAIN LONG, SAWLIKE SPINES.

USED FOR SELF-DEFENSE, THE STINGER IS TIPPED WITH VENOMOUS BARBS THAT CAN RIP THROUGH FLESH. BECAUSE OF THEIR SPINY TAILS, FRESH-WATER STINGRAYS ARE RESPONSIBLE FOR MORE INJURIES TO PEOPLE THAN ANY OTHER AMAZONIAN SPECIES.

ELECTRIC EELS CAN REACH MORE THAN 8 FEET IN LENGTH AND WEIGH OVER 40 POUNDS. THEY LIVE IN SHALLOW, MUDDY WATER AND COME TO THE SURFACE ABOUT EVERY 10 MINUTES TO BREATHE AIR. THEY CAN PRODUCE ENOUGH ELECTRICITY TO ILLUMINATE 12 LIGHTBULBS.

WHAT WE'RE LOOKING AT IS THE RED-BELLIED PIRANHA. THEY'RE NAMED AFTER THE RED ON THEIR UNDERSIDES.
IF YOU LOOK CLOSELY, THIS PIRANHA HAS PROTRUDING JAWBONES WITH LARGE CHOMPING MUSCLES.
WHEN IT CLOSES ITS MOUTH, THE TRIANGULAR KNIFELIKE TEETH FROM BOTH JAWS LOCK TOGETHER LIKE A BEAR TRAP.
THE WORD "*PIRANHA*" LITERALLY TRANSLATES TO "TOOTH FISH."

RRRRRRRRBRMMMMMMMMMM!!RUM-BRUM-BRRRR

PLANTING A TREE IS ANOTHER GREAT WAY TO REPLACE WHAT WE'RE LOSING, NO MATTER WHERE WE LIVE.

IN THAT CASE, I'M GOING TO PLANT TWO TREES! MAYBE EVEN THREE OR FOUR!

THAT'S THE SPIRIT.

RR-BBBRUM-BRUMMMMM!!BRUM-BRRUMBRRRRRRR

WE MAY FEEL WE'RE JUST A SMALL DROP IN THE OCEAN, OR, IN THIS CASE, THE FOREST, BUT TOGETHER WE CAN MAKE A DIFFERENCE.

HEY, LOOK ABOVE ME!

RRRRRRRRRRRRRRRRRBRMMMMMMMMMMM!!

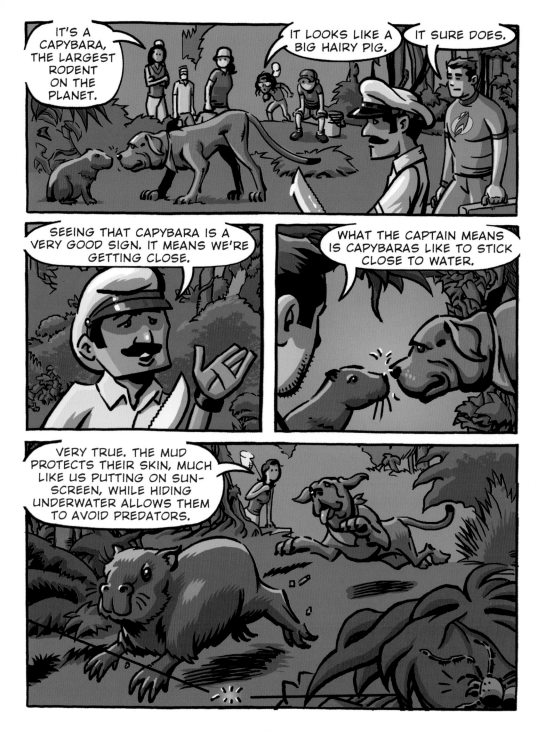

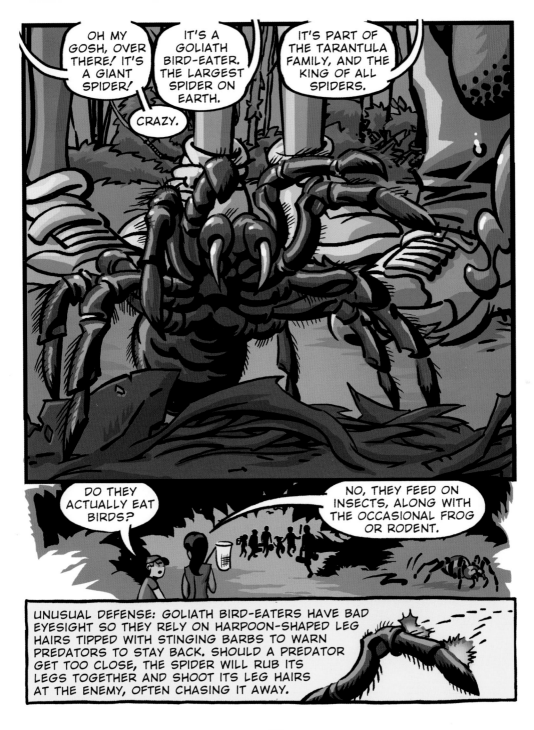

LOOK, THERE'S MORE SMOKE OVER THERE.

ACTUALLY, THAT'S STEAM COMING FROM A POOL OF WATER.

I'VE HEARD ABOUT HOT WATER IN THE AMAZON, LIKE THE BOILING RIVER.

I DIDN'T KNOW THERE'S HOT WATER IN THE AMAZON.

THERE IS WHEN RAINWATER FALLS TO THE GROUND AND SEEPS DEEP BENEATH THE EARTH, WHERE IT'S HEATED AND RESURFACES THROUGH FAULTS AND CRACKS. THERE MUST BE A LARGE CRACK BENEATH THAT POOL.

THE WATER LOOKS SCORCHING HOT.

IT'S PROBABLY 100 OR 200 DEGREES FAHRENHEIT. I BET THE GROUND SURROUNDING THE POOL IS VERY HOT TOO.

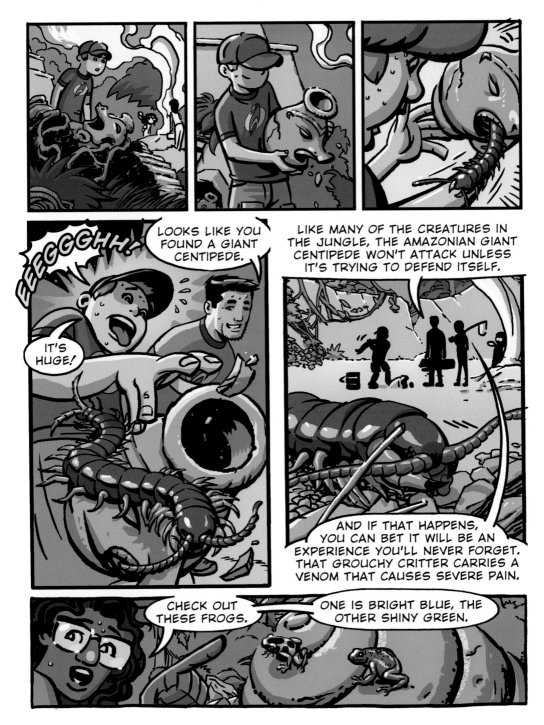

LOOKS LIKE YOU FOUND A GIANT CENTIPEDE.

EEEGGGHH!

IT'S HUGE!

LIKE MANY OF THE CREATURES IN THE JUNGLE, THE AMAZONIAN GIANT CENTIPEDE WON'T ATTACK UNLESS IT'S TRYING TO DEFEND ITSELF.

AND IF THAT HAPPENS, YOU CAN BET IT WILL BE AN EXPERIENCE YOU'LL NEVER FORGET. THAT GROUCHY CRITTER CARRIES A VENOM THAT CAUSES SEVERE PAIN.

CHECK OUT THESE FROGS.

ONE IS BRIGHT BLUE, THE OTHER SHINY GREEN.

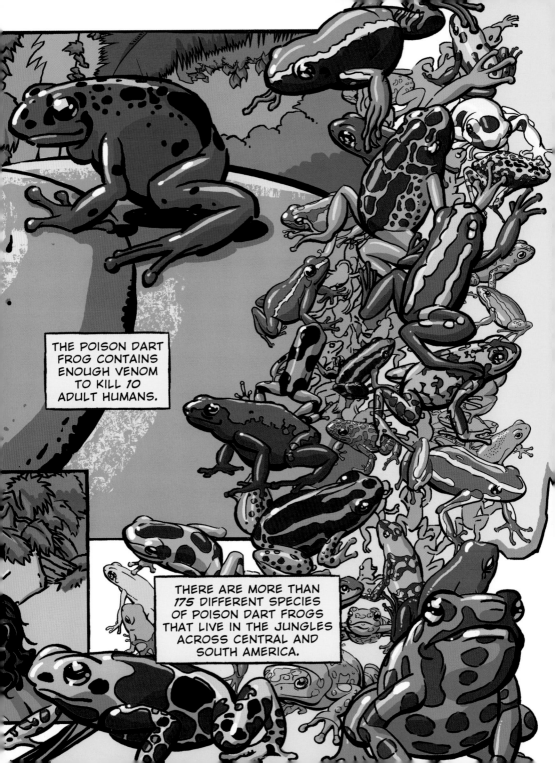

THE POISON DART FROG CONTAINS ENOUGH VENOM TO KILL *10* ADULT HUMANS.

THERE ARE MORE THAN *175* DIFFERENT SPECIES OF POISON DART FROGS THAT LIVE IN THE JUNGLES ACROSS CENTRAL AND SOUTH AMERICA.

THE FROG'S BRIGHT SKIN COLOR IS A WARNING TO ITS PREDATORS. IF ANY PREDATOR TRIES TO EAT IT, THE FROG'S SKIN WILL RELEASE A HIGHLY DANGEROUS POISON.

AND THAT POISON COMES FROM PLANTS CERTAIN INSECTS EAT.

WHEN THESE FROGS EAT THOSE INSECTS, THEY STORE THE POISON, WHICH IS ABSORBED INTO THE FROG'S SKIN. THAT'S HOW THEY BECOME POISON DART FROGS.

POISON DART FROGS ARE FOUND IN MANY STRIKING COLORS, INCLUDING BLUE, RED, GREEN, COPPER, AND GOLD. THE GOLDEN POISON DART FROG IS THE MOST POISONOUS SPECIES OF THE FAMILY, AND THE MOST TOXIC ANIMAL IN THE WORLD.

74

GREEN ANACONDAS ARE FOUND IN SWAMPS, MARSHES, STREAMS, AND RIVERS OF THE AMAZON. THEY CAN GROW TO LENGTHS OF 30 FEET AND WEIGH MORE THAN 500 POUNDS.

SEEMS THE TRAIL CONTINUES ON THE OTHER SIDE. I SAY WE KEEP FOLLOWING IT.

I DO TOO.

ME TOO. WE JUST HAVE TO GET THROUGH THE SWAMPY PART.

THERE'S SOMETHING WATCHING US.

DON'T TELL ME IT'S ANOTHER ANACONDA.

NO, YOU'RE LOOKING AT AN ARAPAIMA, ONE OF THE LARGEST FISHES IN THE WORLD.

THE ARAPAIMA IS A MASSIVE YET SLEEK STREAMLINED FRESHWATER FISH NATIVE TO THE STREAMS OF THE AMAZON RIVER BASIN. IT CAN GROW UP TO 10 FEET IN LENGTH AND WEIGH SEVERAL HUNDRED POUNDS. IT CAN ALSO BREATHE AIR, ALLOWING IT TO SURVIVE IN POOLS WITH LOW WATER LEVELS OR DECAYING VEGETATION. ARAPAIMA CAN SURVIVE UP TO 24 HOURS OUTSIDE THE WATER.

81

84

I'M ALREADY FEELING MUCH BETTER.

THAT WAS FAST.

THE PLANTS IN THE AMAZON, WILL, ARE LIKE MEDICINE.

IT SURE SEEMS THAT WAY.

HOW DID HE KNOW WHAT PLANTS TO USE?

AND HOW DID HE KNOW ENRICO GOT STUNG BY A BULLET ANT?

I'M SURE THE KUKAMA HAVE SEEN IT ALL.

YOU'RE RIGHT ABOUT THAT.

THE KUKAMA LIVE DEEP WITHIN THE RAIN-FOREST, AND THE RAIN-FOREST LIVES DEEP WITHIN THEM.

MANY MEDICINES AND DRUGS USED TO CURE VARIOUS ILLNESSES COME FROM THE PLANTS IN THE AMAZON RAINFOREST.

89

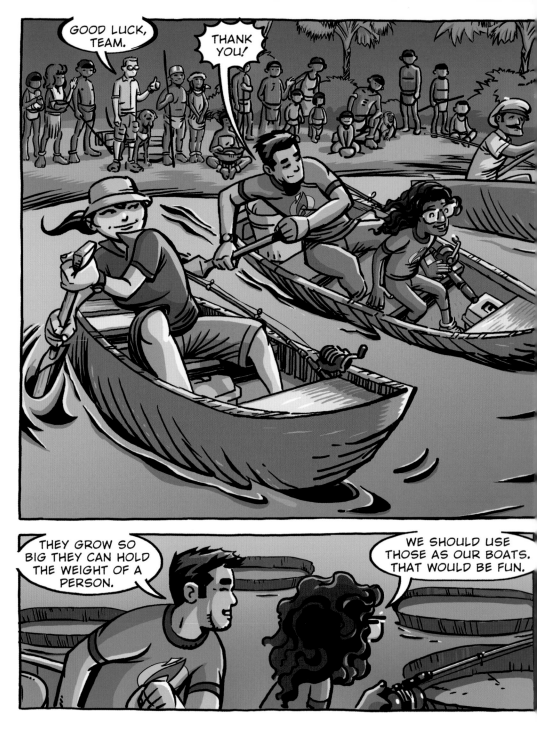

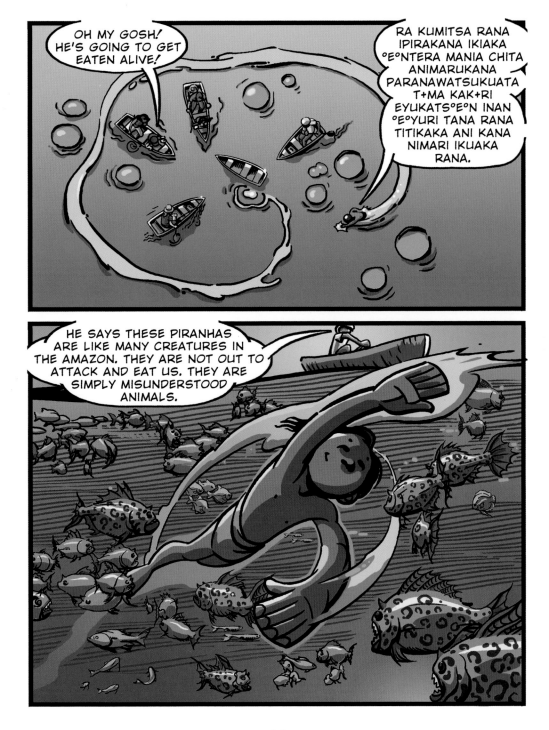

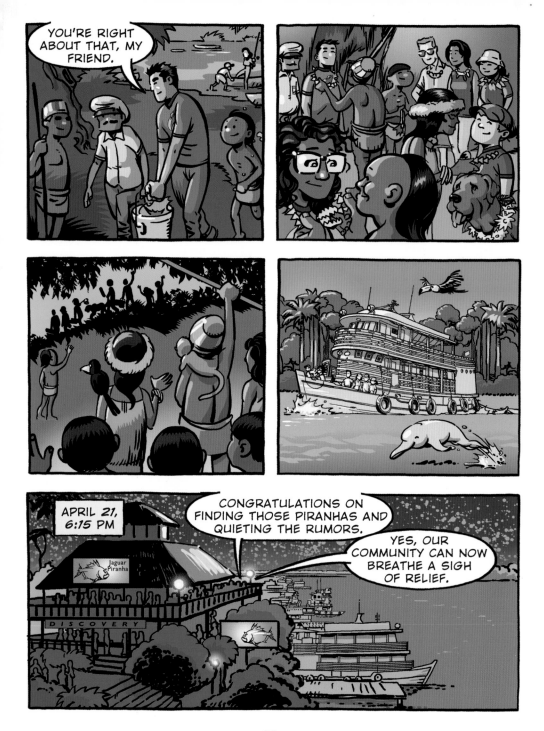

THAT'S GREAT TO HEAR. THANK YOU.

BUT IT'S NOT JUST ABOUT NEW DISCOVERY.

TAIRA'S RIGHT. WE SPOKE WITH THE KUKAMA AND THEY ARE VERY WORRIED ABOUT THEIR HOMES, THEIR FAMILIES, AND THE FUTURE OF THEIR PEOPLE.

WITHOUT QUESTION, WE MUST DO A BETTER JOB OF PROTECTING THEM.

IF I MAY ADD. THE LAYERS OF THE AMAZON ARE ALL INTERCONNECTED, FROM THE RIVERS TO THE FOREST CANOPY TO THE KUKAMA WHO CALL THE RAIN-FOREST HOME.

JUST THINK: A NEW SPECIES BEING FOUND IN ONE PARTICULAR AREA OF THE JUNGLE COULD HELP PROTECT A FOREST AND THOSE WHO LIVE THERE, LIKE THE KUKAMA. THAT'S WHAT GETS US EXCITED.

WHEN I GET HOME, I'M GOING TO SHARE WITH MY PARENTS, MY TEACHERS, AND ALL THE KIDS AT SCHOOL WHAT I LEARNED ON THIS TRIP SO WE CAN HELP SAVE THE AMAZON.

ME TOO!

The authors would like to personally thank:

Karen Wojtyla and the editorial publishing team at Margaret K. McElderry Books and Simon & Schuster Children's Publishing; Paul Beaver at Amazonia Expeditions and Angels of the Amazon; Celeste Taricuarima; Devon Graham, PhD, and Jim Lovins at Project Amazonas Inc.; Tiffany Armstrong; and William Rudd. Special thanks to David Tanguay and Sonya Pelletier for their coloring assistance.

FABIEN COUSTEAU is the grandson of famed sea explorer Jacques Cousteau and champions the family legacy as a third-generation ocean explorer and filmmaker. Learn more about his work at fabiencousteauolc.org.

JAMES O. FRAIOLI is the author of twenty-five books and is an award-winning filmmaker. He has served on the board of directors for the Seattle Aquarium and works with many environmental organizations. Learn more about his work at vesperentertainment.com.

JOE ST.PIERRE has sold more than two million comic books, illustrating and writing for Marvel, DC, and Valiant Comics, as well as his own properties published through his company, Astronaut Ink. Learn more at astronautink.com and popartproperties.com.